ADULTING 101 CHECKLISTS

Copyright 2021 by Lisha Welch

Cover design by Lisha Welch

This book is not intended as financial advice

MONTHLY BUDGET

MONTH OF

TOTAL INCOME	OTHER INCOME / SAVINGS

EXPENSES ITEM	BUDGET	ACTUAL	DIFFERENCE	NOTES
MORTGAGE/RENT				
HOUSEHOLD MAINTENANCE				
TAXES				
INSURANCE				
ELECTRICITY				
WATER				
SEWAGE				
GAS				
PHONE				
TRASH				
CABLE				
CELL PHONE				
GROCERIES				
ENTERTAINMENT				
CHARITY/DONATIONS				
FUEL				
AUTO INSURANCE				
CAR PAYMENT				
CHILD CARE				
CREDIT CARDS/DEBT				
LOANS				
DINING OUT				
SPORTING EVENTS				
LIVE THEATER				
CONCERTS				
MOVIES				
TOTAL EXPENSES				

MONTHLY BUDGET

MONTH OF

TOTAL INCOME			OTHER INCOME / SAVINGS		

EXPENSES ITEM	BUDGET	ACTUAL	DIFFERENCE	NOTES
MORTGAGE/RENT				
HOUSEHOLD MAINTENANCE				
TAXES				
INSURANCE				
ELECTRICITY				
WATER				
SEWAGE				
GAS				
PHONE				
TRASH				
CABLE				
CELL PHONE				
GROCERIES				
ENTERTAINMENT				
CHARITY/DONATIONS				
FUEL				
AUTO INSURANCE				
CAR PAYMENT				
CHILD CARE				
CREDIT CARDS/DEBT				
LOANS				
DINING OUT				
SPORTING EVENTS				
LIVE THEATER				
CONCERTS				
MOVIES				
TOTAL EXPENSES				

MONTHLY BUDGET

MONTH OF

TOTAL INCOME | **OTHER INCOME / SAVINGS**

EXPENSES ITEM	BUDGET	ACTUAL	DIFFERENCE	NOTES
MORTGAGE/RENT				
HOUSEHOLD MAINTENANCE				
TAXES				
INSURANCE				
ELECTRICITY				
WATER				
SEWAGE				
GAS				
PHONE				
TRASH				
CABLE				
CELL PHONE				
GROCERIES				
ENTERTAINMENT				
CHARITY/DONATIONS				
FUEL				
AUTO INSURANCE				
CAR PAYMENT				
CHILD CARE				
CREDIT CARDS/DEBT				
LOANS				
DINING OUT				
SPORTING EVENTS				
LIVE THEATER				
CONCERTS				
MOVIES				
TOTAL EXPENSES				

MONTHLY BUDGET

MONTH OF

TOTAL INCOME		OTHER INCOME / SAVINGS		
EXPENSES ITEM	**BUDGET**	**ACTUAL**	**DIFFERENCE**	**NOTES**
MORTGAGE/RENT				
HOUSEHOLD MAINTENANCE				
TAXES				
INSURANCE				
ELECTRICITY				
WATER				
SEWAGE				
GAS				
PHONE				
TRASH				
CABLE				
CELL PHONE				
GROCERIES				
ENTERTAINMENT				
CHARITY/DONATIONS				
FUEL				
AUTO INSURANCE				
CAR PAYMENT				
CHILD CARE				
CREDIT CARDS/DEBT				
LOANS				
DINING OUT				
SPORTING EVENTS				
LIVE THEATER				
CONCERTS				
MOVIES				
TOTAL EXPENSES				

MONTHLY BUDGET

MONTH OF

TOTAL INCOME		OTHER INCOME / SAVINGS		

EXPENSES ITEM	BUDGET	ACTUAL	DIFFERENCE	NOTES
MORTGAGE/RENT				
HOUSEHOLD MAINTENANCE				
TAXES				
INSURANCE				
ELECTRICITY				
WATER				
SEWAGE				
GAS				
PHONE				
TRASH				
CABLE				
CELL PHONE				
GROCERIES				
ENTERTAINMENT				
CHARITY/DONATIONS				
FUEL				
AUTO INSURANCE				
CAR PAYMENT				
CHILD CARE				
CREDIT CARDS/DEBT				
LOANS				
DINING OUT				
SPORTING EVENTS				
LIVE THEATER				
CONCERTS				
MOVIES				
TOTAL EXPENSES				

MONTHLY BUDGET

MONTH OF

TOTAL INCOME | **OTHER INCOME / SAVINGS**

EXPENSES ITEM	BUDGET	ACTUAL	DIFFERENCE	NOTES
MORTGAGE/RENT				
HOUSEHOLD MAINTENANCE				
TAXES				
INSURANCE				
ELECTRICITY				
WATER				
SEWAGE				
GAS				
PHONE				
TRASH				
CABLE				
CELL PHONE				
GROCERIES				
ENTERTAINMENT				
CHARITY/DONATIONS				
FUEL				
AUTO INSURANCE				
CAR PAYMENT				
CHILD CARE				
CREDIT CARDS/DEBT				
LOANS				
DINING OUT				
SPORTING EVENTS				
LIVE THEATER				
CONCERTS				
MOVIES				
TOTAL EXPENSES				

MONTHLY BUDGET

MONTH OF

TOTAL INCOME   **OTHER INCOME / SAVINGS**

EXPENSES ITEM	BUDGET	ACTUAL	DIFFERENCE	NOTES
MORTGAGE/RENT				
HOUSEHOLD MAINTENANCE				
TAXES				
INSURANCE				
ELECTRICITY				
WATER				
SEWAGE				
GAS				
PHONE				
TRASH				
CABLE				
CELL PHONE				
GROCERIES				
ENTERTAINMENT				
CHARITY/DONATIONS				
FUEL				
AUTO INSURANCE				
CAR PAYMENT				
CHILD CARE				
CREDIT CARDS/DEBT				
LOANS				
DINING OUT				
SPORTING EVENTS				
LIVE THEATER				
CONCERTS				
MOVIES				
TOTAL EXPENSES				

MONTHLY BUDGET

MONTH OF

TOTAL INCOME			OTHER INCOME / SAVINGS	

EXPENSES ITEM	BUDGET	ACTUAL	DIFFERENCE	NOTES
MORTGAGE/RENT				
HOUSEHOLD MAINTENANCE				
TAXES				
INSURANCE				
ELECTRICITY				
WATER				
SEWAGE				
GAS				
PHONE				
TRASH				
CABLE				
CELL PHONE				
GROCERIES				
ENTERTAINMENT				
CHARITY/DONATIONS				
FUEL				
AUTO INSURANCE				
CAR PAYMENT				
CHILD CARE				
CREDIT CARDS/DEBT				
LOANS				
DINING OUT				
SPORTING EVENTS				
LIVE THEATER				
CONCERTS				
MOVIES				
TOTAL EXPENSES				

MONTHLY BUDGET

MONTH OF

TOTAL INCOME   **OTHER INCOME / SAVINGS**

EXPENSES ITEM	BUDGET	ACTUAL	DIFFERENCE	NOTES
MORTGAGE/RENT				
HOUSEHOLD MAINTENANCE				
TAXES				
INSURANCE				
ELECTRICITY				
WATER				
SEWAGE				
GAS				
PHONE				
TRASH				
CABLE				
CELL PHONE				
GROCERIES				
ENTERTAINMENT				
CHARITY/DONATIONS				
FUEL				
AUTO INSURANCE				
CAR PAYMENT				
CHILD CARE				
CREDIT CARDS/DEBT				
LOANS				
DINING OUT				
SPORTING EVENTS				
LIVE THEATER				
CONCERTS				
MOVIES				
TOTAL EXPENSES				

MONTHLY BUDGET

MONTH OF

TOTAL INCOME

OTHER INCOME / SAVINGS

EXPENSES ITEM	BUDGET	ACTUAL	DIFFERENCE	NOTES
MORTGAGE/RENT				
HOUSEHOLD MAINTENANCE				
TAXES				
INSURANCE				
ELECTRICITY				
WATER				
SEWAGE				
GAS				
PHONE				
TRASH				
CABLE				
CELL PHONE				
GROCERIES				
ENTERTAINMENT				
CHARITY/DONATIONS				
FUEL				
AUTO INSURANCE				
CAR PAYMENT				
CHILD CARE				
CREDIT CARDS/DEBT				
LOANS				
DINING OUT				
SPORTING EVENTS				
LIVE THEATER				
CONCERTS				
MOVIES				
TOTAL EXPENSES				

MONTHLY BUDGET

MONTH OF

TOTAL INCOME

OTHER INCOME / SAVINGS

EXPENSES ITEM	BUDGET	ACTUAL	DIFFERENCE	NOTES
MORTGAGE/RENT				
HOUSEHOLD MAINTENANCE				
TAXES				
INSURANCE				
ELECTRICITY				
WATER				
SEWAGE				
GAS				
PHONE				
TRASH				
CABLE				
CELL PHONE				
GROCERIES				
ENTERTAINMENT				
CHARITY/DONATIONS				
FUEL				
AUTO INSURANCE				
CAR PAYMENT				
CHILD CARE				
CREDIT CARDS/DEBT				
LOANS				
DINING OUT				
SPORTING EVENTS				
LIVE THEATER				
CONCERTS				
MOVIES				
TOTAL EXPENSES				

MONTHLY BUDGET

MONTH OF

TOTAL INCOME			OTHER INCOME / SAVINGS		

EXPENSES ITEM	BUDGET	ACTUAL	DIFFERENCE	NOTES
MORTGAGE/RENT				
HOUSEHOLD MAINTENANCE				
TAXES				
INSURANCE				
ELECTRICITY				
WATER				
SEWAGE				
GAS				
PHONE				
TRASH				
CABLE				
CELL PHONE				
GROCERIES				
ENTERTAINMENT				
CHARITY/DONATIONS				
FUEL				
AUTO INSURANCE				
CAR PAYMENT				
CHILD CARE				
CREDIT CARDS/DEBT				
LOANS				
DINING OUT				
SPORTING EVENTS				
LIVE THEATER				
CONCERTS				
MOVIES				
TOTAL EXPENSES				

MONTHLY BILL TRACKER
MONTH: _____

MARK DUE DATE FOR EACH BILL OF THE MONTH

NOTES:

PRIORITY:

☐ _____

☐ _____

☐ _____

☐ _____

☐ _____

S	M	T	W	T	F	S

PAID ☐   PAID ☐   PAID ☐   PAID ☐   PAID ☐   PAID ☐   PAID ☐

PAID ☐   PAID ☐   PAID ☐   PAID ☐   PAID ☐   PAID ☐   PAID ☐

PAID ☐   PAID ☐   PAID ☐   PAID ☐   PAID ☐   PAID ☐   PAID ☐

PAID ☐   PAID ☐   PAID ☐   PAID ☐   PAID ☐   PAID ☐   PAID ☐

PAID ☐   PAID ☐   PAID ☐   PAID ☐   PAID ☐   PAID ☐   PAID ☐

MONTHLY BILL TRACKER
MONTH: _____

MARK DUE DATE FOR EACH BILL OF THE MONTH

NOTES:

PRIORITY:

☐ _____

☐ _____

☐ _____

☐ _____

☐ _____

S	M	T	W	T	F	S

PAID ☐   PAID ☐   PAID ☐   PAID ☐   PAID ☐   PAID ☐   PAID ☐

PAID ☐   PAID ☐   PAID ☐   PAID ☐   PAID ☐   PAID ☐   PAID ☐

PAID ☐   PAID ☐   PAID ☐   PAID ☐   PAID ☐   PAID ☐   PAID ☐

PAID ☐   PAID ☐   PAID ☐   PAID ☐   PAID ☐   PAID ☐   PAID ☐

PAID ☐   PAID ☐   PAID ☐   PAID ☐   PAID ☐   PAID ☐   PAID ☐

MONTHLY BILL TRACKER
MONTH: _____

MARK DUE DATE FOR EACH BILL OF THE MONTH

NOTES:

PRIORITY:

☐ _____

☐ _____

☐ _____

☐ _____

☐ _____

S	M	T	W	T	F	S

PAID ☐   PAID ☐   PAID ☐   PAID ☐   PAID ☐   PAID ☐   PAID ☐

PAID ☐   PAID ☐   PAID ☐   PAID ☐   PAID ☐   PAID ☐   PAID ☐

PAID ☐   PAID ☐   PAID ☐   PAID ☐   PAID ☐   PAID ☐   PAID ☐

PAID ☐   PAID ☐   PAID ☐   PAID ☐   PAID ☐   PAID ☐   PAID ☐

PAID ☐   PAID ☐   PAID ☐   PAID ☐   PAID ☐   PAID ☐   PAID ☐

MONTHLY BILL TRACKER
MONTH: _____

MARK DUE DATE FOR EACH BILL OF THE MONTH

NOTES:

PRIORITY:

☐ _____

☐ _____

☐ _____

☐ _____

☐ _____

S	M	T	W	T	F	S

PAID ☐   PAID ☐   PAID ☐   PAID ☐   PAID ☐   PAID ☐   PAID ☐

PAID ☐   PAID ☐   PAID ☐   PAID ☐   PAID ☐   PAID ☐   PAID ☐

PAID ☐   PAID ☐   PAID ☐   PAID ☐   PAID ☐   PAID ☐   PAID ☐

PAID ☐   PAID ☐   PAID ☐   PAID ☐   PAID ☐   PAID ☐   PAID ☐

PAID ☐   PAID ☐   PAID ☐   PAID ☐   PAID ☐   PAID ☐   PAID ☐

MONTHLY BILL TRACKER
MONTH: _____

MARK DUE DATE FOR EACH BILL OF THE MONTH

NOTES:

PRIORITY:

☐ _____

☐ _____

☐ _____

☐ _____

☐ _____

S	M	T	W	T	F	S

PAID ☐ PAID ☐ PAID ☐ PAID ☐ PAID ☐ PAID ☐ PAID ☐

PAID ☐ PAID ☐ PAID ☐ PAID ☐ PAID ☐ PAID ☐ PAID ☐

PAID ☐ PAID ☐ PAID ☐ PAID ☐ PAID ☐ PAID ☐ PAID ☐

PAID ☐ PAID ☐ PAID ☐ PAID ☐ PAID ☐ PAID ☐ PAID ☐

PAID ☐ PAID ☐ PAID ☐ PAID ☐ PAID ☐ PAID ☐ PAID ☐

MONTHLY BILL TRACKER
MONTH: _____

MARK DUE DATE FOR EACH BILL OF THE MONTH

NOTES:

PRIORITY:

☐ _____

☐ _____

☐ _____

☐ _____

☐ _____

S	M	T	W	T	F	S

PAID ☐   PAID ☐   PAID ☐   PAID ☐   PAID ☐   PAID ☐   PAID ☐

PAID ☐   PAID ☐   PAID ☐   PAID ☐   PAID ☐   PAID ☐   PAID ☐

PAID ☐   PAID ☐   PAID ☐   PAID ☐   PAID ☐   PAID ☐   PAID ☐

PAID ☐   PAID ☐   PAID ☐   PAID ☐   PAID ☐   PAID ☐   PAID ☐

PAID ☐   PAID ☐   PAID ☐   PAID ☐   PAID ☐   PAID ☐   PAID ☐

MONTHLY BILL TRACKER
MONTH: _____

MARK DUE DATE FOR EACH BILL OF THE MONTH

NOTES:

PRIORITY:

☐ _____

☐ _____

☐ _____

☐ _____

☐ _____

S	M	T	W	T	F	S

PAID ☐ PAID ☐ PAID ☐ PAID ☐ PAID ☐ PAID ☐ PAID ☐

PAID ☐ PAID ☐ PAID ☐ PAID ☐ PAID ☐ PAID ☐ PAID ☐

PAID ☐ PAID ☐ PAID ☐ PAID ☐ PAID ☐ PAID ☐ PAID ☐

PAID ☐ PAID ☐ PAID ☐ PAID ☐ PAID ☐ PAID ☐ PAID ☐

PAID ☐ PAID ☐ PAID ☐ PAID ☐ PAID ☐ PAID ☐ PAID ☐

MONTHLY BILL TRACKER
MONTH: _____
MARK DUE DATE FOR EACH BILL OF THE MONTH

NOTES:

PRIORITY:

☐ _____

☐ _____

☐ _____

☐ _____

☐ _____

S	M	T	W	T	F	S
PAID ☐	PAID ☐	PAID ☐	PAID ☐	PAID ☐	PAID ☐	PAID ☐
PAID ☐	PAID ☐	PAID ☐	PAID ☐	PAID ☐	PAID ☐	PAID ☐
PAID ☐	PAID ☐	PAID ☐	PAID ☐	PAID ☐	PAID ☐	PAID ☐
PAID ☐	PAID ☐	PAID ☐	PAID ☐	PAID ☐	PAID ☐	PAID ☐
PAID ☐	PAID ☐	PAID ☐	PAID ☐	PAID ☐	PAID ☐	PAID ☐

MONTHLY BILL TRACKER
MONTH: _____

MARK DUE DATE FOR EACH BILL OF THE MONTH

NOTES:

PRIORITY:

- [ ] _____
- [ ] _____
- [ ] _____
- [ ] _____
- [ ] _____

S	M	T	W	T	F	S

PAID ☐ PAID ☐ PAID ☐ PAID ☐ PAID ☐ PAID ☐ PAID ☐

PAID ☐ PAID ☐ PAID ☐ PAID ☐ PAID ☐ PAID ☐ PAID ☐

PAID ☐ PAID ☐ PAID ☐ PAID ☐ PAID ☐ PAID ☐ PAID ☐

PAID ☐ PAID ☐ PAID ☐ PAID ☐ PAID ☐ PAID ☐ PAID ☐

PAID ☐ PAID ☐ PAID ☐ PAID ☐ PAID ☐ PAID ☐ PAID ☐

MONTHLY BILL TRACKER
MONTH: _____

MARK DUE DATE FOR EACH BILL OF THE MONTH

NOTES:

PRIORITY:

☐ _____

☐ _____

☐ _____

☐ _____

☐ _____

S	M	T	W	T	F	S

PAID ☐ PAID ☐ PAID ☐ PAID ☐ PAID ☐ PAID ☐ PAID ☐

PAID ☐ PAID ☐ PAID ☐ PAID ☐ PAID ☐ PAID ☐ PAID ☐

PAID ☐ PAID ☐ PAID ☐ PAID ☐ PAID ☐ PAID ☐ PAID ☐

PAID ☐ PAID ☐ PAID ☐ PAID ☐ PAID ☐ PAID ☐ PAID ☐

PAID ☐ PAID ☐ PAID ☐ PAID ☐ PAID ☐ PAID ☐ PAID ☐

MONTHLY BILL TRACKER
MONTH: _____

MARK DUE DATE FOR EACH BILL OF THE MONTH

NOTES:

PRIORITY:

☐ _____

☐ _____

☐ _____

☐ _____

☐ _____

S	M	T	W	T	F	S

PAID ☐   PAID ☐   PAID ☐   PAID ☐   PAID ☐   PAID ☐   PAID ☐

PAID ☐   PAID ☐   PAID ☐   PAID ☐   PAID ☐   PAID ☐   PAID ☐

PAID ☐   PAID ☐   PAID ☐   PAID ☐   PAID ☐   PAID ☐   PAID ☐

PAID ☐   PAID ☐   PAID ☐   PAID ☐   PAID ☐   PAID ☐   PAID ☐

PAID ☐   PAID ☐   PAID ☐   PAID ☐   PAID ☐   PAID ☐   PAID ☐

MONTHLY BILL TRACKER
MONTH: _____

MARK DUE DATE FOR EACH BILL OF THE MONTH

NOTES:

PRIORITY:

☐ _____

☐ _____

☐ _____

☐ _____

☐ _____

S	M	T	W	T	F	S
PAID ☐	PAID ☐	PAID ☐	PAID ☐	PAID ☐	PAID ☐	PAID ☐
PAID ☐	PAID ☐	PAID ☐	PAID ☐	PAID ☐	PAID ☐	PAID ☐
PAID ☐	PAID ☐	PAID ☐	PAID ☐	PAID ☐	PAID ☐	PAID ☐
PAID ☐	PAID ☐	PAID ☐	PAID ☐	PAID ☐	PAID ☐	PAID ☐
PAID ☐	PAID ☐	PAID ☐	PAID ☐	PAID ☐	PAID ☐	PAID ☐

UTILITIES TRACKER

Company Name: _____

Account Number: _____

Due date: _____

Customer Service Number: _____

Emergency Number: _____

Billing Address: _____

URL: _____

Username: _____

Password:_____

Notes: _____

_____

_____

_____

Company Name: _____

Account Number: _____

Due date: _____

Customer Service Number: _____

Emergency Number: _____

Billing Address: _____

URL: _____

Username: _____

Password:_____

Notes: _____

_____

_____

_____

Company Name: _____

Account Number: _____

Due date: _____

Customer Service Number: _____

Emergency Number: _____

Billing Address: _____

URL: _____

Username: _____

Password:_____

Notes: _____

_____

_____

_____

Company Name: _____

Account Number: _____

Due date: _____

Customer Service Number: _____

Emergency Number: _____

Billing Address: _____

URL: _____

Username: _____

Password:_____

Notes: _____

_____

_____

_____

Company Name: _____

Account Number: _____

Due date: _____

Customer Service Number: _____

Emergency Number: _____

Billing Address: _____

URL: _____

Username: _____

Password:_____

Notes: _____

_____

_____

_____

Company Name: _____

Account Number: _____

Due date: _____

Customer Service Number: _____

Emergency Number: _____

Billing Address: _____

URL: _____

Username: _____

Password:_____

Notes: _____

_____

_____

_____

UTILITIES TRACKER

Company Name: _____
Account Number: _____
Due date: _____
Customer Service Number: _____
Emergency Number: _____
Billing Address: _____
URL: _____
Username: _____
Password: _____
Notes: _____
_____
_____
_____

Company Name: _____
Account Number: _____
Due date: _____
Customer Service Number: _____
Emergency Number: _____
Billing Address: _____
URL: _____
Username: _____
Password: _____
Notes: _____
_____
_____
_____

Company Name: _____
Account Number: _____
Due date: _____
Customer Service Number: _____
Emergency Number: _____
Billing Address: _____
URL: _____
Username: _____
Password: _____
Notes: _____
_____
_____
_____

Company Name: _____
Account Number: _____
Due date: _____
Customer Service Number: _____
Emergency Number: _____
Billing Address: _____
URL: _____
Username: _____
Password: _____
Notes: _____
_____
_____
_____

Company Name: _____
Account Number: _____
Due date: _____
Customer Service Number: _____
Emergency Number: _____
Billing Address: _____
URL: _____
Username: _____
Password: _____
Notes: _____
_____
_____
_____

Company Name: _____
Account Number: _____
Due date: _____
Customer Service Number: _____
Emergency Number: _____
Billing Address: _____
URL: _____
Username: _____
Password: _____
Notes: _____
_____
_____
_____

SAVINGS TRACKER

SAVING FOR	START	END	GOAL

DATE	MEMO	WITHDRAWAL	DEPOSIT	BALANCE

SAVINGS TRACKER

SAVING FOR	START	END	GOAL

DATE	MEMO	WITHDRAWAL	DEPOSIT	BALANCE

DEBT TRACKER

TYPE	MIN. PAYMENT	TOTAL PAYMENT	DUE

PAID	BALANCE	PAID	BALANCE

DEBT TRACKER

TYPE	MIN. PAYMENT	TOTAL PAYMENT	DUE

PAID	BALANCE	PAID	BALANCE

SUBSCRIPTION TRACKER

ORGANIZATION	DATE PAID	AMOUNT	DURATION	EXP. DATE	RENEW DATE	RENEW METHOD

PASSWORD TRACKER

SITE	USERNAME	PASSWORD

PASSWORD TRACKER

SITE	USERNAME	PASSWORD

TO DO LIST

Top Priorities

1 _____
2 _____
3 _____
4 _____

Appointments

1 _____
2 _____
3 _____
4 _____

Today's To-Do

☐ _____
☐ _____
☐ _____
☐ _____
☐ _____
☐ _____
☐ _____

Tomorrow To-Do

☐ _____
☐ _____
☐ _____
☐ _____
☐ _____
☐ _____
☐ _____

Notes

Doodle

TO DO LIST

Top Priorities

1. _____
2. _____
3. _____
4. _____

Appointments

1. _____
2. _____
3. _____
4. _____

Today's To-Do

- [ ] _____
- [ ] _____
- [ ] _____
- [ ] _____
- [ ] _____
- [ ] _____
- [ ] _____

Tomorrow To-Do

- [ ] _____
- [ ] _____
- [ ] _____
- [ ] _____
- [ ] _____
- [ ] _____
- [ ] _____

Notes

Doodle

TO DO LIST

Top Priorities

1 _____
2 _____
3 _____
4 _____

Appointments

1 _____
2 _____
3 _____
4 _____

Today's To-Do

☐ _____
☐ _____
☐ _____
☐ _____
☐ _____
☐ _____
☐ _____

Tomorrow To-Do

☐ _____
☐ _____
☐ _____
☐ _____
☐ _____
☐ _____
☐ _____

Notes

Doodle

TO DO LIST

Top Priorities

1 _____
2 _____
3 _____
4 _____

Appointments

1 _____
2 _____
3 _____
4 _____

Today's To-Do

☐ _____
☐ _____
☐ _____
☐ _____
☐ _____
☐ _____
☐ _____

Tomorrow To-Do

☐ _____
☐ _____
☐ _____
☐ _____
☐ _____
☐ _____
☐ _____

Notes

Doodle

TO DO LIST

Top Priorities

1. _____
2. _____
3. _____
4. _____

Appointments

1. _____
2. _____
3. _____
4. _____

Today's To-Do

- ☐ _____
- ☐ _____
- ☐ _____
- ☐ _____
- ☐ _____
- ☐ _____
- ☐ _____

Tomorrow To-Do

- ☐ _____
- ☐ _____
- ☐ _____
- ☐ _____
- ☐ _____
- ☐ _____
- ☐ _____

Notes

Doodle

BIRTHDAY REMINDERS

JANUARY	FEBRUARY	MARCH
APRIL	MAY	JUNE
JULY	AUGUST	SEPTEMBER
OCTOBER	NOVEMBER	DECEMBER

BIRTHDAY REMINDERS

JANUARY

FEBRUARY

MARCH

APRIL

MAY

JUNE

JULY

AUGUST

SEPTEMBER

OCTOBER

NOVEMBER

DECEMBER

WEEKLY CHORE CHART

CHORES

	M	T	W	T
_____	☐	☐	☐	☐
_____	☐	☐	☐	☐
_____	☐	☐	☐	☐
_____	☐	☐	☐	☐
_____	☐	☐	☐	☐
_____	☐	☐	☐	☐
_____	☐	☐	☐	☐	☐	☐
_____	☐	☐	☐	☐	☐	☐

NOTES

WEEKLY CHORE CHART

CHORES

	M	T	W	T		
_____	☐	☐	☐	☐		
_____	☐	☐	☐	☐		
_____	☐	☐	☐	☐		
_____	☐	☐	☐	☐		
_____	☐	☐	☐	☐		
_____	☐	☐	☐	☐		
_____	☐	☐	☐	☐	☐	☐
_____	☐	☐	☐	☐	☐	☐

NOTES

WEEKLY CHORE CHART

CHORES

	M	T	W	T		
	☐	☐	☐	☐		
	☐	☐	☐	☐		
	☐	☐	☐	☐		
	☐	☐	☐	☐		
	☐	☐	☐	☐		
	☐	☐	☐	☐		
	☐	☐	☐	☐	☐	☐
	☐	☐	☐	☐	☐	☐

NOTES

WEEKLY CHORE CHART

CHORES

	M	T	W	T		
	☐	☐	☐	☐		
	☐	☐	☐	☐		
	☐	☐	☐	☐		
	☐	☐	☐	☐		
	☐	☐	☐	☐		
	☐	☐	☐	☐		
	☐	☐	☐	☐	☐	☐
	☐	☐	☐	☐	☐	☐

NOTES

WEEKLY CHORE CHART

CHORES

	M	T	W	T		
_____	☐	☐	☐	☐		
_____	☐	☐	☐	☐		
_____	☐	☐	☐	☐		
_____	☐	☐	☐	☐		
_____	☐	☐	☐	☐		
_____	☐	☐	☐	☐		
_____	☐	☐	☐	☐	☐	☐
_____	☐	☐	☐	☐	☐	☐

NOTES

WEEKLY CHORE CHART

CHORES

	M	T	W	T		
_____	☐	☐	☐	☐		
_____	☐	☐	☐	☐		
_____	☐	☐	☐	☐		
_____	☐	☐	☐	☐		
_____	☐	☐	☐	☐		
_____	☐	☐	☐	☐		
_____	☐	☐	☐	☐	☐	☐
_____	☐	☐	☐	☐	☐	☐

NOTES

WEEKLY CHORE CHART

CHORES

	M	T	W	T		
_____	☐	☐	☐	☐		
_____	☐	☐	☐	☐		
_____	☐	☐	☐	☐		
_____	☐	☐	☐	☐		
_____	☐	☐	☐	☐		
_____	☐	☐	☐	☐		
_____	☐	☐	☐	☐	☐	☐
_____	☐	☐	☐	☐	☐	☐

NOTES

WEEKLY CHORE CHART

CHORES

	M	T	W	T		
_____	☐	☐	☐	☐		
_____	☐	☐	☐	☐		
_____	☐	☐	☐	☐		
_____	☐	☐	☐	☐		
_____	☐	☐	☐	☐		
_____	☐	☐	☐	☐		
_____	☐	☐	☐	☐	☐	☐
_____	☐	☐	☐	☐	☐	☐

NOTES

GROCERY LIST

FRESH PRODUCE

_____
_____
_____
_____
_____
_____
_____
_____
_____
_____
_____
_____
_____
_____
_____
_____
_____
_____

CANNED GOODS

_____
_____
_____
_____
_____
_____
_____

FROZEN FOOD

_____
_____
_____
_____
_____
_____
_____
_____
_____

OTHERS

_____
_____
_____
_____
_____
_____
_____

DAIRY

_____
_____
_____
_____
_____
_____
_____

BREAD/CEREAL

_____
_____
_____
_____
_____
_____
_____
_____
_____
_____
_____

CONDIMENTS

_____
_____
_____
_____
_____
_____
_____
_____

GROCERY LIST

FRESH PRODUCE

_____
_____
_____
_____
_____
_____
_____
_____
_____
_____
_____
_____
_____

CANNED GOODS

_____
_____
_____
_____
_____

FROZEN FOOD

_____
_____
_____
_____
_____
_____
_____

DAIRY

_____
_____
_____
_____

BREAD/CEREAL

_____
_____
_____
_____
_____
_____
_____

CONDIMENTS

_____
_____
_____
_____
_____

OTHERS

_____
_____
_____
_____
_____

GROCERY LIST

FRESH PRODUCE

_____
_____
_____
_____
_____
_____
_____
_____
_____
_____
_____
_____
_____
_____
_____
_____
_____

CANNED GOODS

_____
_____
_____
_____
_____
_____

FROZEN FOOD

_____
_____
_____
_____
_____
_____
_____
_____
_____

OTHERS

_____
_____
_____
_____
_____
_____

DAIRY

_____
_____
_____
_____
_____

BREAD/CEREAL

_____
_____
_____
_____
_____
_____
_____
_____
_____
_____

CONDIMENTS

_____
_____
_____
_____
_____
_____

GROCERY LIST

FRESH PRODUCE

_____
_____
_____
_____
_____
_____
_____
_____
_____
_____
_____
_____
_____
_____
_____
_____
_____

CANNED GOODS

_____
_____
_____
_____
_____
_____
_____
_____

FROZEN FOOD

_____
_____
_____
_____
_____
_____
_____
_____
_____

OTHERS

_____
_____
_____
_____
_____
_____
_____

CONDIMENTS

_____
_____
_____
_____
_____
_____
_____

DAIRY

_____
_____
_____
_____
_____
_____
_____
_____

BREAD/CEREAL

_____
_____
_____
_____
_____
_____
_____
_____
_____
_____
_____

GROCERY LIST

FRESH PRODUCE

_____
_____
_____
_____
_____
_____
_____
_____
_____
_____
_____
_____
_____
_____
_____

CONDIMENTS

_____
_____
_____
_____
_____
_____
_____

CANNED GOODS

_____
_____
_____
_____
_____
_____

FROZEN FOOD

_____
_____
_____
_____
_____
_____
_____
_____

OTHERS

_____
_____
_____
_____
_____
_____
_____

DAIRY

_____
_____
_____
_____
_____
_____

BREAD/CEREAL

_____
_____
_____
_____
_____
_____
_____
_____
_____

GROCERY LIST

FRESH PRODUCE

_____
_____
_____
_____
_____
_____
_____
_____
_____
_____
_____
_____
_____

CONDIMENTS

_____
_____
_____
_____
_____

CANNED GOODS

_____
_____
_____
_____
_____
_____

FROZEN FOOD

_____
_____
_____
_____
_____
_____

OTHERS

_____
_____
_____
_____

DAIRY

_____
_____
_____
_____
_____

BREAD/CEREAL

_____
_____
_____
_____
_____
_____
_____
_____

GROCERY LIST

FRESH PRODUCE

_____
_____
_____
_____
_____
_____
_____
_____
_____
_____
_____
_____

CONDIMENTS

_____
_____
_____
_____
_____
_____

CANNED GOODS

_____
_____
_____
_____
_____

FROZEN FOOD

_____
_____
_____
_____
_____
_____
_____

OTHERS

_____
_____
_____
_____
_____
_____

DAIRY

_____
_____
_____
_____
_____

BREAD/CEREAL

_____
_____
_____
_____
_____
_____
_____
_____
_____
_____
_____

GROCERY LIST

FRESH PRODUCE

_____
_____
_____
_____
_____
_____
_____
_____
_____
_____
_____
_____
_____
_____
_____
_____
_____
_____

CONDIMENTS

_____
_____
_____
_____
_____
_____
_____

CANNED GOODS

_____
_____
_____
_____
_____
_____
_____

FROZEN FOOD

_____
_____
_____
_____
_____
_____
_____
_____
_____
_____

OTHERS

_____
_____
_____
_____
_____
_____
_____

DAIRY

_____
_____
_____
_____
_____
_____
_____

BREAD/CEREAL

_____
_____
_____
_____
_____
_____
_____
_____
_____
_____
_____
_____

WEEKLY MEAL PLANNER

Breakfast   Lunch   Dinner

S

M

T

W

TH

F

S

WEEKLY MEAL PLANNER

Breakfast   Lunch   Dinner

S

M

T

W

TH

F

S

WEEKLY MEAL PLANNER

Breakfast   Lunch   Dinner

S

M

T

W

TH

F

S

WEEKLY MEAL PLANNER

Breakfast   Lunch   Dinner

S
_____

M
_____

T
_____

W
_____

TH
_____

F
_____

S
_____

WEEKLY MEAL PLANNER

Breakfast   Lunch   Dinner

S

M

T

W

TH

F

S

WEEKLY MEAL PLANNER

Breakfast   Lunch   Dinner

S
_____

M
_____

T
_____

W
_____

TH
_____

F
_____

S
_____

WEEKLY MEAL PLANNER

Breakfast   Lunch   Dinner

S
_____

M
_____

T
_____

W
_____

TH
_____

F
_____

S
_____

WEEKLY MEAL PLANNER

Breakfast   Lunch   Dinner

S

_____

M

_____

T

_____

W

_____

TH

_____

F

_____

S

_____

WEEKLY MEAL PLANNER

Breakfast   Lunch   Dinner

S

M

T

W

TH

F

S

WEEKLY MEAL PLANNER

Breakfast   Lunch   Dinner

S
_____

M
_____

T
_____

W
_____

TH
_____

F
_____

S
_____

WEEKLY MEAL PLANNER

Breakfast   Lunch   Dinner

S
_____

M
_____

T
_____

W
_____

TH
_____

F
_____

S
_____

WEEKLY MEAL PLANNER

Breakfast   Lunch   Dinner

S
_____

M
_____

T
_____

W
_____

TH
_____

F
_____

S
_____

WEEKLY MEAL PLANNER

Breakfast   Lunch   Dinner

S

_____

M

_____

T

_____

W

_____

TH

_____

F

_____

S

_____

WEEKLY MEAL PLANNER

Breakfast   Lunch   Dinner

S

M

T

W

TH

F

S

DAILY GOAL

MAIN GOAL: ○ ○ ○ ○

BRIEF:

SECONDARY GOALS:

CHALLENGE:

THINGS TO DO:

☐ .... ☐ .... ☐ ....
☐ .... ☐ .... ☐ ....
☐ .... ☐ .... ☐ ....

NOTES:

DAILY GOAL

MAIN GOAL: ○ ○ ○ ○

....
....
....

BRIEF:

_____

_____

_____

_____

_____

_____

_____

SECONDARY GOALS:

CHALLENGE:

THINGS TO DO:

- ☐ ....
- ☐ ....
- ☐ ....
- ☐ ....
- ☐ ....
- ☐ ....
- ☐ ....
- ☐ ....
- ☐ ....

NOTES:

....
....
....

DAILY GOAL

MAIN GOAL: ○ ○ ○ ○

....
....
....

BRIEF:

_____
_____
_____
_____
_____
_____
_____

SECONDARY GOALS:

CHALLENGE:

THINGS TO DO:

☐ .... ☐ .... ☐ ....
☐ .... ☐ .... ☐ ....
☐ .... ☐ .... ☐ ....

NOTES:

....
....
....

DAILY GOAL

MAIN GOAL: ○ ○ ○ ○

BRIEF:

SECONDARY GOALS:

CHALLENGE:

THINGS TO DO:

- [ ] ....
- [ ] ....
- [ ] ....
- [ ] ....
- [ ] ....
- [ ] ....
- [ ] ....
- [ ] ....
- [ ] ....

NOTES:

DAILY GOAL

MAIN GOAL: ○ ○ ○ ○

BRIEF:

SECONDARY GOALS:

CHALLENGE:

THINGS TO DO:

- ☐ ....
- ☐ ....
- ☐ ....
- ☐ ....
- ☐ ....
- ☐ ....
- ☐ ....
- ☐ ....
- ☐ ....

NOTES:

DAILY GOAL

MAIN GOAL: ○ ○ ○ ○

BRIEF:

SECONDARY GOALS:

CHALLENGE:

THINGS TO DO:

- ☐ ....
- ☐ ....
- ☐ ....
- ☐ ....
- ☐ ....
- ☐ ....
- ☐ ....
- ☐ ....
- ☐ ....

NOTES:

DAILY GOAL

MAIN GOAL: ○ ○ ○ ○

BRIEF:

SECONDARY GOALS:

CHALLENGE:

THINGS TO DO:

- ☐ ....
- ☐ ....
- ☐ ....
- ☐ ....
- ☐ ....
- ☐ ....
- ☐ ....
- ☐ ....
- ☐ ....

NOTES:

DAILY GOAL

MAIN GOAL: ○ ○ ○ ○

BRIEF:

SECONDARY GOALS:

CHALLENGE:

THINGS TO DO:

☐ ....   ☐ ....   ☐ ....

☐ ....   ☐ ....   ☐ ....

☐ ....   ☐ ....   ☐ ....

NOTES:

DAILY GOAL

MAIN GOAL: ○ ○ ○ ○

BRIEF:

SECONDARY GOALS:

CHALLENGE:

THINGS TO DO:

- [ ] ....
- [ ] ....
- [ ] ....
- [ ] ....
- [ ] ....
- [ ] ....
- [ ] ....
- [ ] ....
- [ ] ....

NOTES:

DAILY GOAL

MAIN GOAL: ○ ○ ○ ○

BRIEF:

SECONDARY GOALS:

CHALLENGE:

THINGS TO DO:

☐ .... ☐ .... ☐ ....

☐ .... ☐ .... ☐ ....

☐ .... ☐ .... ☐ ....

NOTES:

DAILY GOAL

MAIN GOAL: ○ ○ ○ ○

....

....

....

BRIEF:

_____

_____

_____

_____

_____

_____

_____

SECONDARY GOALS:

CHALLENGE:

THINGS TO DO:

☐ .... ☐ .... ☐ ....

☐ .... ☐ .... ☐ ....

☐ .... ☐ .... ☐ ....

NOTES:

....

....

....

DAILY GOAL

MAIN GOAL: ○ ○ ○ ○

BRIEF:

SECONDARY GOALS:

CHALLENGE:

THINGS TO DO:

☐ .... ☐ .... ☐ ....
☐ .... ☐ .... ☐ ....
☐ .... ☐ .... ☐ ....

NOTES:

DAILY GOAL

MAIN GOAL:　　　　　　　　　　　○ ○ ○ ○

....

....

....

BRIEF:

_____

_____

_____

_____

_____

_____

_____

SECONDARY GOALS:

CHALLENGE:

THINGS TO DO:

☐ ....　　☐ ....　　☐ ....

☐ ....　　☐ ....　　☐ ....

☐ ....　　☐ ....　　☐ ....

NOTES:

....

....

....

DAILY GOAL

MAIN GOAL: ◯ ◯ ◯ ◯

....
....
....

BRIEF:

_____

_____

_____

_____

_____

_____

_____

SECONDARY GOALS:

CHALLENGE:

THINGS TO DO:

☐ ....   ☐ ....   ☐ ....

☐ ....   ☐ ....   ☐ ....

☐ ....   ☐ ....   ☐ ....

NOTES:

....
....
....

YEARLY GOALS

January
- ○ _____
- ○ _____
- ○ _____
- ○ _____

February
- ○ _____
- ○ _____
- ○ _____
- ○ _____

March
- ○ _____
- ○ _____
- ○ _____
- ○ _____

April
- ○ _____
- ○ _____
- ○ _____
- ○ _____

May
- ○ _____
- ○ _____
- ○ _____
- ○ _____

June
- ○ _____
- ○ _____
- ○ _____
- ○ _____

July
- ○ _____
- ○ _____
- ○ _____
- ○ _____

August
- ○ _____
- ○ _____
- ○ _____
- ○ _____

September
- ○ _____
- ○ _____
- ○ _____
- ○ _____

October
- ○ _____
- ○ _____
- ○ _____
- ○ _____

November
- ○ _____
- ○ _____
- ○ _____
- ○ _____

December
- ○ _____
- ○ _____
- ○ _____
- ○ _____

YEARLY GOALS

January
- ○ _____
- ○ _____
- ○ _____
- ○ _____

February
- ○ _____
- ○ _____
- ○ _____
- ○ _____

March
- ○ _____
- ○ _____
- ○ _____
- ○ _____

April
- ○ _____
- ○ _____
- ○ _____
- ○ _____

May
- ○ _____
- ○ _____
- ○ _____
- ○ _____

June
- ○ _____
- ○ _____
- ○ _____
- ○ _____

July
- ○ _____
- ○ _____
- ○ _____
- ○ _____

August
- ○ _____
- ○ _____
- ○ _____
- ○ _____

September
- ○ _____
- ○ _____
- ○ _____
- ○ _____

October
- ○ _____
- ○ _____
- ○ _____
- ○ _____

November
- ○ _____
- ○ _____
- ○ _____
- ○ _____

December
- ○ _____
- ○ _____
- ○ _____
- ○ _____

MY NOTES

MY NOTES

MY NOTES

MY NOTES

MY NOTES

MY NOTES

MY NOTES

MY NOTES

MY NOTES

MY NOTES

MY NOTES

Made in United States
North Haven, CT
28 August 2022

23394032R00057